Does God Like To Color?

Second Edition

Shana M. Joyner

Truth In Fiction Books
https://truthinfictionbooks.com
Round Rock, Texas, USA

Does God Like To Color, 2nd edition

Published by Truth In Fiction Books (an imprint of Mind Activation Code LLC, Texas, USA).

Visit https://truthinfictionbooks.com for free coloring pages and more.

ISBN-13 (Paperback): 978-1-943994-18-2
ISBN-13 (Kindle): 978-1-943994-19-9
ISBN-13 (EPUB): 978-1-943994-20-5

Library of Congress Control Number: 2020920154

DEDICATION

Thank you Father God for all the awesome things you have done.

I dedicate this book to children in all nations everywhere. May you know the love of God and always be curious.

"Let the little children come to Me, and do not forbid them; for of such is the kingdom of God."
– Mark 10:14

It was a rainy day. Isaac and Ruth could not go out and play. They had to stay in the house.

5

"Do you have paper?" asked Mom.

"We do,"
said Isaac.

"Do you have pencils and crayons?" asked Dad.

"We do," said Ruth.

Isaac and Ruth gathered their supplies. They sat down at the table with Mom and Dad. Everybody began to color.

They colored
and colored
and colored
some more.

But then...

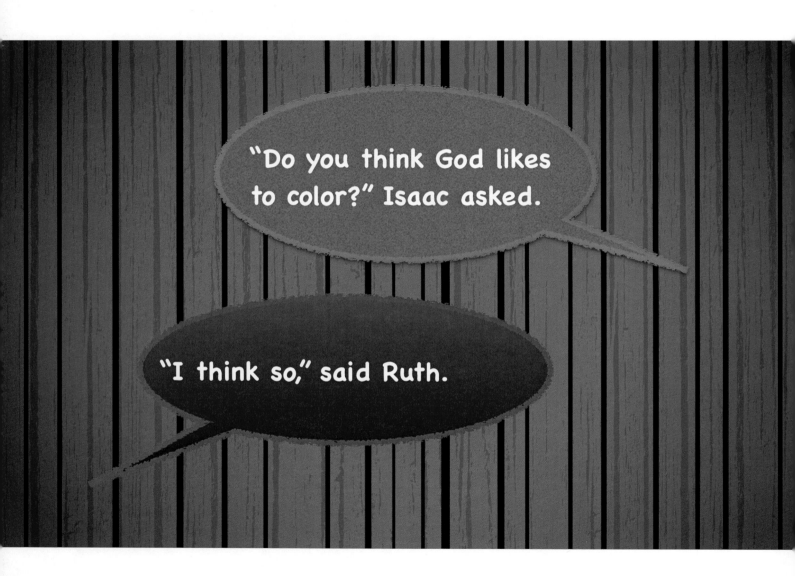

"That's a good question...Hmmm.
Let's think about it..." said Dad.

"Let's make a list of our
ideas," said Mom.

So, they made a list of what they thought.

On their list, they said...

God likes to color
with black for
outer space
where he hangs
the stars and the
planets.

God likes to
color in blue.
See the sky and
the ocean.

God also colors
with white for
the clouds in
the sky and the
foamy tips of
the waves.

God likes to color with brown for soil in the garden and sand at the beach.

God likes to color in green. Look at the grass and the leafy plants that feed us.

God likes to color with red.

God likes to color in pink too.

Think about the beautiful roses.

God likes to color with purple for the grapes.

Isaac also added that grapes make yummy jelly for his belly.

They do indeed.

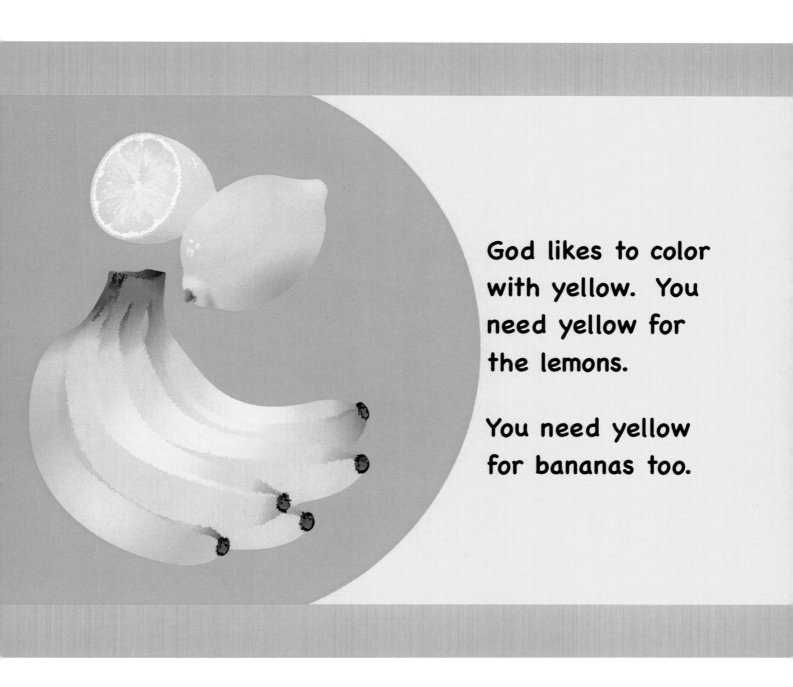

God likes to color with yellow. You need yellow for the lemons.

You need yellow for bananas too.

God likes to color
with orange for
oranges and for
the warm bright
sun.

But sometimes...
just sometimes...
God colors with
gray for the
rainy days.

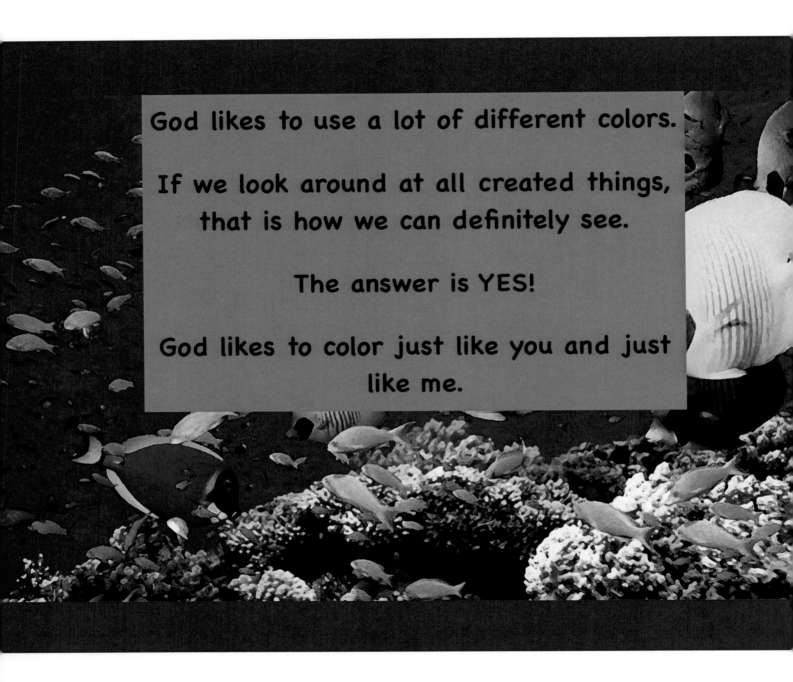

God likes to use a lot of different colors.

If we look around at all created things, that is how we can definitely see.

The answer is YES!

God likes to color just like you and just like me.

What colors do you see?

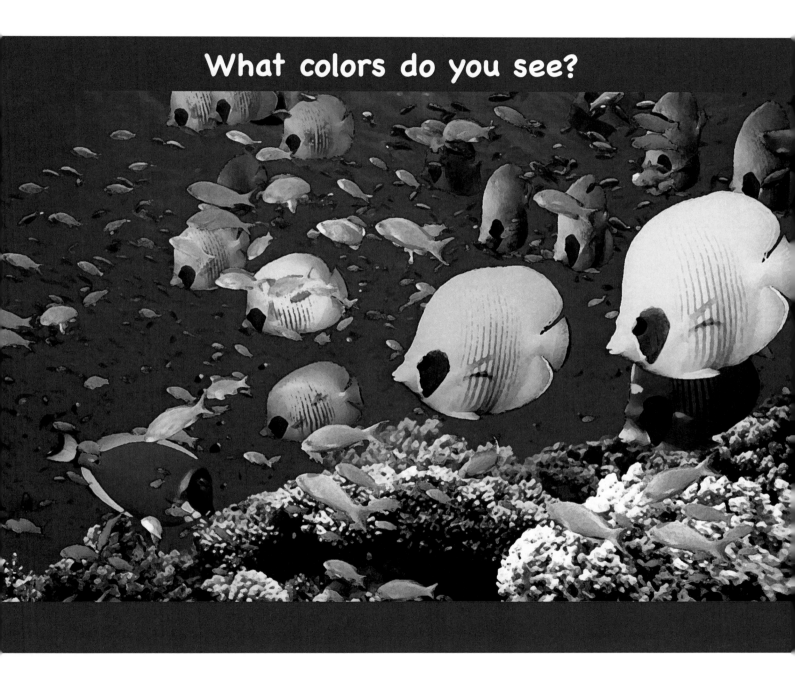

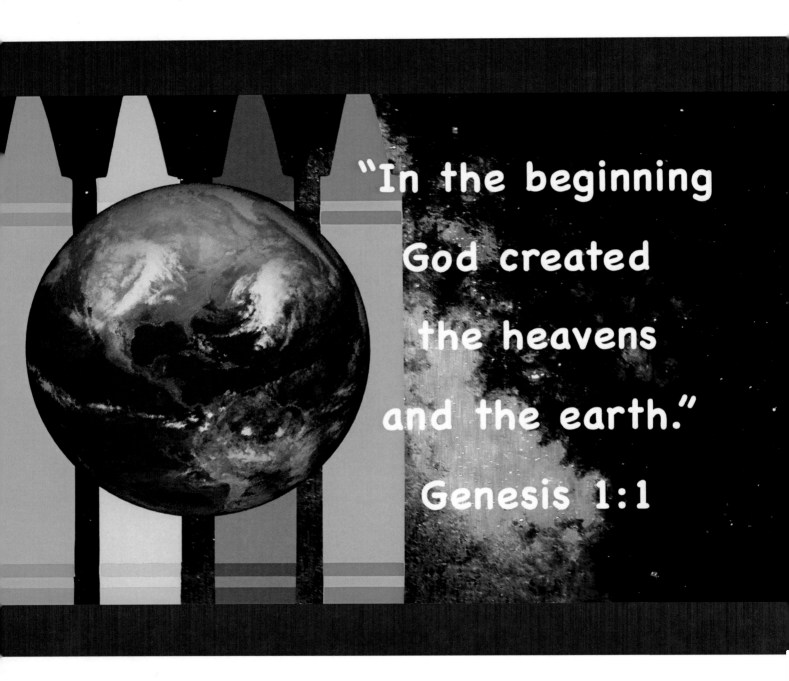

Thank you God for creating a big beautiful colorful world.

Amen

Made in United States
North Haven, CT
15 February 2022

16139640R00015